LISTENING SKILLS
LEVEL 4

OPTIONS
PUBLISHING
inc.

All rights reserved. No part of this document may be reproduced or used in any form or by any means—graphic, electronic, or mechanical, including photocopying, recording, taping, and information storage and retrieval systems.

ISBN 1-56936-677-2
© 2000 Options Publishing, Inc.
P.O. Box 1749
Merrimack, NH 03054-1749
All rights reserved.
Printed in the United States of America
10 9 8

Table of Contents

	Page
Lesson 1 Listening for a Purpose	2
Lesson 2 Listening to a News Story—The Hale-Bopp Comet	4
Lesson 3 Listening to a News Story—The Exxon Valdez Disaster	6
Lesson 4 Listening to a Science Article—Clouds	8
Lesson 5 Listening to a Science Article—Starfish	10
Lesson 6 Listening to a Social Studies Article—Antarctica	12
Lesson 7 Listening to a Social Studies Article—Stars and Stripes	14
Lesson 8 Listening to a Character Sketch—from A Door Near Here	16
Lesson 9 Listening to a Character Sketch—from Owen Foote, Soccer Star	18
Lesson 10 Listening to a Folktale—Buffalo Hunt	20
Lesson 11 Listening to a Folktale—Why Bat is an Animal	22
Lesson 12 Listening to a Folktale—The Boy Who Snared the Wind	24
Lesson 13 Practice Test—Fat Sheep, Lean Sheep, and Senor Coyote	26

Lesson 1 Listening for a Purpose

When you read or hear a story or non-fiction article, think about what the author is trying to do. For example, the author might want to show a comparison between two things. Or, the author might want to explain a cause and effect relationship, tell about a sequence of events, or make a statement and give an example.

Here are samples of short passages from the stories and articles you will listen to as you work through this book. The charts show how the ideas or information fit together.

Statement and Example

Starfish come in many colors. The Cushion Star has brown, orange, red, and yellow colors.

Statement	Example
Starfish come in many colors.	The Cushion Star has

Cause and Effect

Because Alan Hale and Thomas Bopp both discovered the comet at about the same time, both men were awarded discovery of the comet.

Cause

Effect

both men awarded discovery of comet

Listening Skills 4

2

Comparison

The amount of moisture that Antarctica receives per year is similar to the hottest deserts of the world. But, unlike other deserts, Antarctica's moisture falls as snow, not rain.

Comparison of Antarctica and the World's Hottest Deserts	
similarities	differences
very little moisture falls	

Sequence

The first step was to pump unspoiled oil from the tanker. Then the ship was removed.

1.	2. Ship was removed.

Listen and Think

Listen as your teacher reads some short passages. For each passage, circle the phrase that best tells about how the sentences are related.

1. statement and example   cause and effect   comparison   sequence
2. statement and example   cause and effect   comparison   sequence
3. statement and example   cause and effect   comparison   sequence
4. statement and example   cause and effect   comparison   sequence
5. statement and example   cause and effect   comparison   sequence

LESSON 2 Listening to a News Story

The Hale-Bopp Comet

News stories are often written to answer the **five w** and **h**-questions: who? what? when? where? why? and how? Listen to this news story about the discovery of a comet.

Tips for Listening
- Follow the events of the story in your mind—listen for the answers to the **five w** and **h**-questions.
- Think about the answer to "why?"—it's usually the main idea.

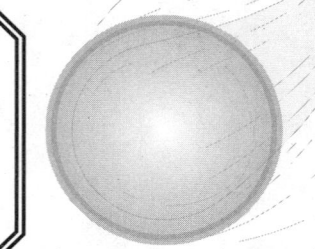

Listen and Think

Listen as your teacher reads the news story, "The Hale-Bopp Comet."

Here are the vocabulary words you need to know from the story.

observatory — a place where scientists look at the night sky

cluster — a group

amateur stargazer — a person whose hobby is looking at stars

Answering the w and h-questions

Complete this chart with answers to the **w** and **h**-questions as you listen to the story for the second time.

who?	
what?	two people found a new comet
when?	July 23, 1995
where?	
why?	new comets are named after the people who discover them
how?	looking through telescopes

Listening Skills 4

4

Distinguishing Main Idea and Details

The main idea of the news story is written in the center of the web below. Complete the web by writing four facts or details from the story that support the main idea.

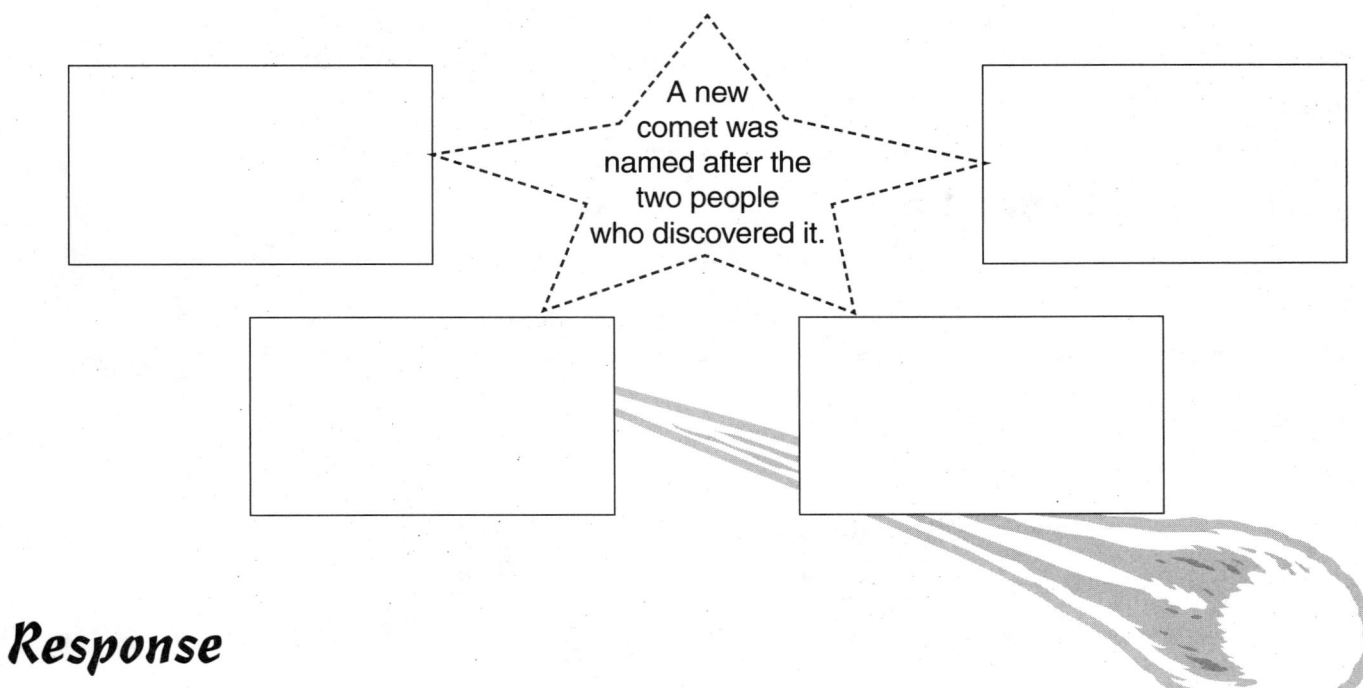

A new comet was named after the two people who discovered it.

Response

Identifying Facts and Details

1. According to the story, which man is an "amateur stargazer"?
   A. Alan Hale
   B. Thomas Bopp
   C. Hale-Bopp
2. This story takes place in
   A. winter.
   B. spring.
   C. summer.

Summarizing

3. Write two sentences telling the story of the discovery of the Hale-Bopp Comet in your own words.

_____
_____
_____

Lesson 3 Listening to a News Story

The Exxon Valdez Disaster

News stories often tell about events that are related. The news story you will hear in this lesson tells about what happened when a ship carrying oil ran aground off the coast of Alaska.

Tips for Listening
- Listen for time words and other clues to sequence.
- Try not to think about other things while you are listening.

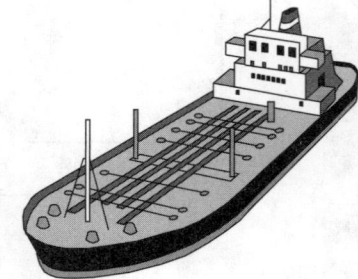

Listen and Think

Listen as your teacher reads the news story, "The Exxon Valdez Disaster."

Here are the vocabulary words you need to know from the story.

oil tanker — a huge ship that transports tons of oil.

catastrophe — a disaster

Understanding Sequence of Events

Keep track of the main events of the story in a sequence chart. Complete the chart below as you listen to the story for the second time.

Sequence Chart

The Accident	The Cleanup	Years Later

listening Skills 4

Identifying Cause and Effect Relationships

Write a phrase or sentence to identify the effect.

Cause and Effect Chart

Cause

Strong winds carry the oil many miles along the shoreline.

Effect

Response

Summarizing

1. List at least three ways the oil spill was cleaned up.

   _____
   _____
   _____

2. List at least three animals that were affected by the disaster.

   _____
   _____

Using Context Clues

3. Write a word or phrase telling what "nooks and crannies" are.

   _____
   _____

4. Write a sentence telling what it means for a ship to "run aground."

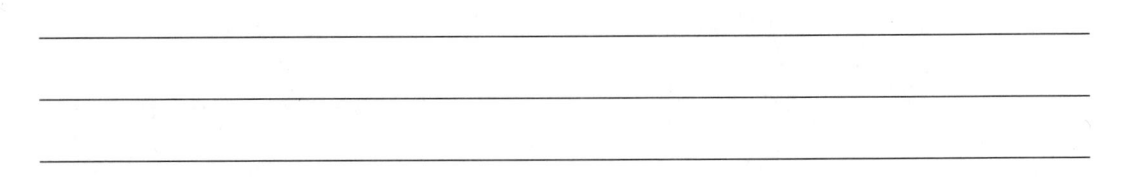

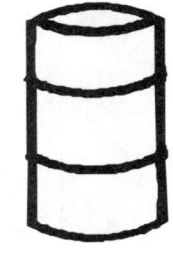

   _____
   _____

Listening Skills 4

LESSON

4 Listening to a Science Article

CLOUDS

Articles that report scientific facts and information often begin with a statement of the main idea, and then follow with examples. The article you will hear in this lesson is about clouds.

Tips for Listening
- Listen for the main idea statement in the beginning of the article.
- Keep a mental checklist as you listen for the examples which follow.

Listen and Think

Listen as your teacher reads the science article "Clouds."

Here are the vocabulary words you need to know for this article.

droplet — a tiny drop of liquid

overcast — clouded over, dark gray

Distinguishing Main Idea and Details

Separate the main idea from supporting details using a statement and example chart. Complete the one below as you listen to the article for the second time.

Statement and Example Chart

Statement	Examples
There are three main types of clouds.	1.
	2.
	3.

Listening Skills 4

8

© 2000 Options Publishing, Inc. No part of this document may be reproduced without the written permission of the publisher

Comparing and Contrasting

Complete the chart below to compare the different types of clouds.

Comparison Chart

	Height	Description
Cirrus		
Stratus		
Cumulus		

Response

Identifying Facts and Details

1. Which type of cloud produces no rain?
    A. cirrus
    B. stratonimbus
    C. cumulonimbus

2. Which type of cloud produces lightening and thunder?
    A. cirrus
    B. stratonimbus
    C. cumulonimbus

Making Inferences

3. If you look up in the sky and see an elephant in the clouds, you are probably looking at
    A. cirrus clouds.
    B. stratus clouds.
    C. cumulus clouds.
    D. nimbus clouds.

Listening Skills 4

Lesson 5 Listening to a Science Article

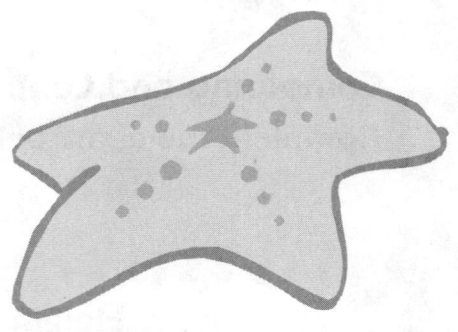

Starfish

Articles about scientific topics often use comparisons. The article you will hear in this lesson is about fish and starfish.

Tips for Listening
- Keep your eyes on the speaker.
- Ask yourself questions as you listen.

Listen and Think

Listen as your teacher reads the science article, "Starfish."

Here are the vocabulary words you need to know from the article.

invertebrate — having no skeleton inside the body

plankton — very small creatures that live in sea water

Comparing and Contrasting

Write words or phrases to chart how fish and starfish are alike and different.

Fish and Starfish

similarities	differences

Listening Skills 4

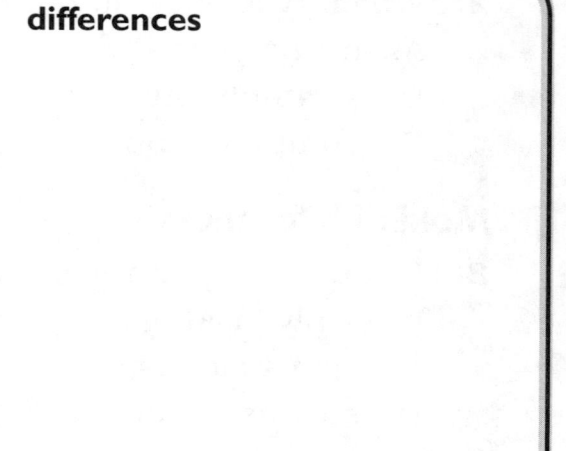

Summarizing

Write a few sentences comparing and contrasting fish and starfish. Use the chart that you completed on page 10 for ideas and information.

Cause and Effect Chart

Cause	Effect

Response

Identifying Facts and Details

1. All starfish have
    A. forty-four arms.
    B. five or fewer arms.
    C. twenty-four arms.
    D. five or more arms.

Making Inferences

2. Both fish and starfish
    A. come in many colors.
    B. move using tube feet.
    C. move using fins.
    D. have scaly skin.

3. Because they have no fins, starfish probably
    A. can't move sideways.
    B. don't swim as fast as fish.
    C. spend their lives out of water.
    D. catch insects at the surface.

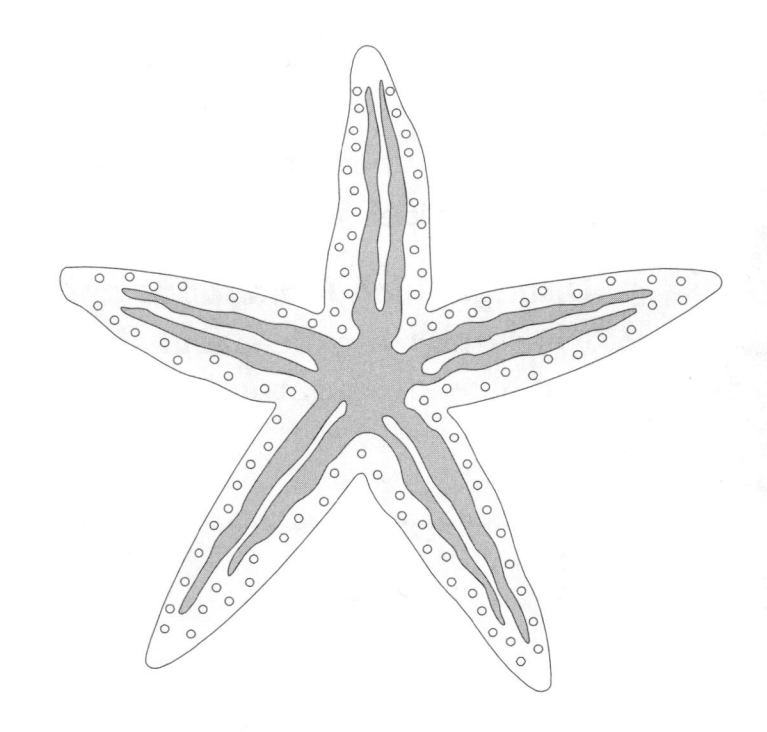

LESSON 6 Listening to a Social Studies Article

Antarctica: The World's Biggest Desert

Factual reports often begin with a question which is then answered in the body of the report. In this lesson, you will hear a social studies article about Antarctica.

Tips for Listening
- Focus. Devote your full attention to what is being said.
- Listen for facts that support statements.

Listen and Think

Listen as your teacher reads the social studies article, "Antarctica: The World's Biggest Desert"

Here are the vocabulary words you need to know from the article.

moisture — a small amount of liquid

elevation — the height of something

archipelago — a chain of islands

Distinguishing Main Ideas and Details

Chart the main ideas and supporting details. Complete the one below as you listen to the article for a second time.

Antarctica

Main Idea	Supporting Detail
Antarctica is a desert.	
It is the coldest continent.	
It is about 5 million sq. miles.	
It holds 90% of all ice.	
Many plants and animals call it home.	

Listening Skills 4

© 2000 Options Publishing, Inc. No part of this document may be reproduced without the written permission of the publisher

Summarizing

Write a few sentences summarizing what you know about Antarctica. Use the chart that you completed on page 12 for ideas and information.

_____
_____
_____
_____

Response

Comparing and Contrasting

1. Antarctica receives about as much moisture as
    A. the Arctic circle.
    B. the world's coldest place.
    C. the world's hottest deserts.
    D. coastal mountains and cliffs.

2. Antarctica is the only desert where all moisture falls as
    A. rain.
    B. hail.
    C. snow.
    D. ice.

3. Which pair of words best describe Antarctica?
    A. windiest and wettest
    B. driest and coldest
    C. hottest and windiest
    D. hottest and coldest

Making Inferences

4. Write a phrase or sentence telling why it is hard to tell Antarctica's exact size.

_____
_____
_____

Lesson 7 Listening to a Social Studies Article

Stars and Stripes

People who write about history can often disagree with each other. The article you will hear in this lesson tells the story of Betsy Ross who sewed the first flag of the United States. Or, did she?

Tips for Listening
- Listen for dates and other clues about time and the order in which things happen.
- If your mind begins to wander, remind yourself of the purpose of the talk or presentation.

Listen and Think

Listen as your teacher reads the social studies article, "Stars and Stripes."

Here are the vocabulary words you need to know from the article.

- **rough sketch** — a simple drawing
- **Philadelphian** — a person who lives in Philadelphia, a city in Pennsylvania
- **seamstress** — a person who is very good at sewing

Understanding Sequence of Events

Keep track of the main events of the story in a sequence chart. Complete the one below as you listen to the story for a second time.

Sequence Chart

How Betsy Ross Sewed the First U.S. Flag		
Washington's Drawing		June 14, 1777–

Listening Skills 4

14

Organizing Information

No one knows for sure if Betsy Ross really sewed the first flag of the United States. There is some evidence that she did, and some that she didn't. Complete the chart below about the evidence.

The Betsy Ross Story

evidence that she sewed the first flag	evidence that she didn't sew the first flag
papers signed by her daughter, granddaughter, and niece	

Response

Making Inferences

1. If the story of Betsy Ross is true, it is likely that George Washington wanted the flag to
   A. be shaped as a circle.
   B. be red, green, and blue.
   C. have vertical stripes.
   D. have six-pointed stars.

2. According to the article, five-pointed stars are
   A. easier to make than six-pointed stars.
   B. harder to make than six-pointed stars.
   C. easier to arrange than six-pointed stars.
   D. favored by Congress.

Summarizing

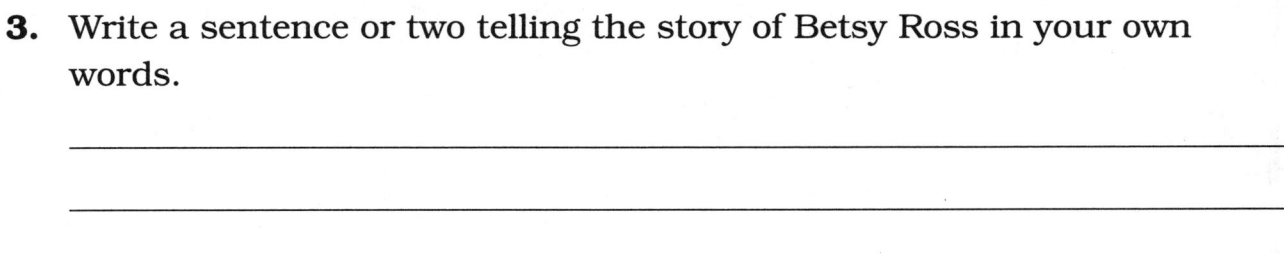

3. Write a sentence or two telling the story of Betsy Ross in your own words.

   _____
   _____
   _____

LESSON 8 Listening to a Character Sketch

from *A Door Near Here*
by Heather G. Quarles

When listening to a story, pay attention to plot—what happens, setting—where the story takes place, and characters. In a story, a character's actions tell a lot about what sort of person he or she is. The character sketch you will hear in this lesson is about a girl who is helping her brothers and sisters get ready for school.

Tips for Listening
- Think about the character's actions. Follow what your character does, and think about the kind of person he or she is.
- If your mind wanders, refocus.

Listen and Think

Listen as your teacher reads the character sketch, *A Door Near Here*, by Heather G. Quarles

Here are the vocabulary words you need to know from the character sketch.

oblivious — forgetful or unmindful

state of chaos — very messy

Identifying Story Elements

Keep track of plot, setting, and characters in a story elements chart. Complete the one below as you listen to the story for a second time.

Story Elements

Plot—What Happens?	Setting—Where?	Characters—Who?

Listening Skills 4

Understanding Text and Structure

The narrator of the character sketch says that she had a lot on her mind. She was trying to do several things at once. List two examples in the chart below.

Statement and Example Chart

Statement	Examples
"Besides, I had about eight hundred things on my mind that morning."	1.
	2.

Response

Understanding Character

1. Which fact from the character sketch suggests that the narrator is a high school student?
   A. She's studying for a chemistry test.
   B. She takes the school bus.
   C. She has a sister in third grade.
   D. She's making sandwiches.

Understanding Setting

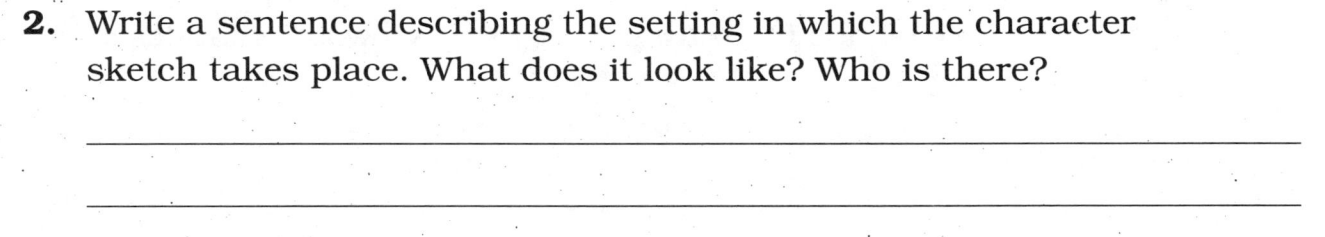

2. Write a sentence describing the setting in which the character sketch takes place. What does it look like? Who is there?

   _____
   _____
   _____

Understanding Plot

3. What does Elisa give to her sister?

   _____

Lesson 9 Listening to a Character Sketch

from *Owen Foote, Soccer Star*

by Stephanie Greene

The character sketch you will hear in this lesson is about a boy who is interested in animals. He compares himself to one of the animals he reads about.

Tips for Listening

- Listen with an open attitude. Uncross your arms and legs. Face the speaker. Sit up straight. Maintain eye contact.
- Pay attention to non-verbal messages. Listen to the speaker's tone of voice and watch his or her facial expressions.

Listen and Think

Listen as your teacher reads the character sketch, *Owen Foote, Soccer Star* by Stephanie Greene.

Here are the vocabulary words you need to know from the character sketch.

crouched — squatted, kneeled down

amphibians — animals that live partly in the water and partly on land.

Understanding Story Elements

The setting of a character sketch is the place where the story takes place. As you listen to the character sketch for the second time, jot down some words and phrases that describe the setting. Also jot down words that describe Owen Foote.

Setting	Characters
	Owen Foote

Listening Skills 4

18

Understanding Character

1. All week Owen had been reading about
    A. soccer.
    B. reptiles.
    C. leopards.
    D. gorillas.

2. Which thought made Owen shiver?
    A. Gorillas are peaceful animals.
    B. The silverback could tear a leopard apart with his bare hands.
    C. Putting on his cleats made him feel ten feet tall.
    D. Gorillas are the greatest.

3. At the beginning of the story, Owen was probably pretending to be a
    A. dolphin.
    B. leopard.
    C. soccer star.
    D. silverback.

Response

Drawing Conclusions

1. Write two or three sentences telling how young gorillas treat the silverback who leads the gorilla family.

    _____
    _____
    _____

2. Owen says that he knows how the young gorillas feel. In what way does soccer make him feel the same?

    _____
    _____
    _____
    _____

LESSON

10 Listening to a Folktale

Buffalo Hunt

Folktales from many different cultures include animal characters who are clever and, smart, and try to control things. In this Native American folktale, we learn that some animals can be smarter than people.

Tips for Listening

- Make connections as you listen. Do any of the characters remind you of others you have heard about?
- Be quiet as you listen. Let the speaker's words fill the space around you.

Listen and Think

Listen as your teacher reads the folktale, "The Buffalo Hunt."

Here is a vocabulary word you need to know from the folktale.

council — a meeting where important matters are decided.

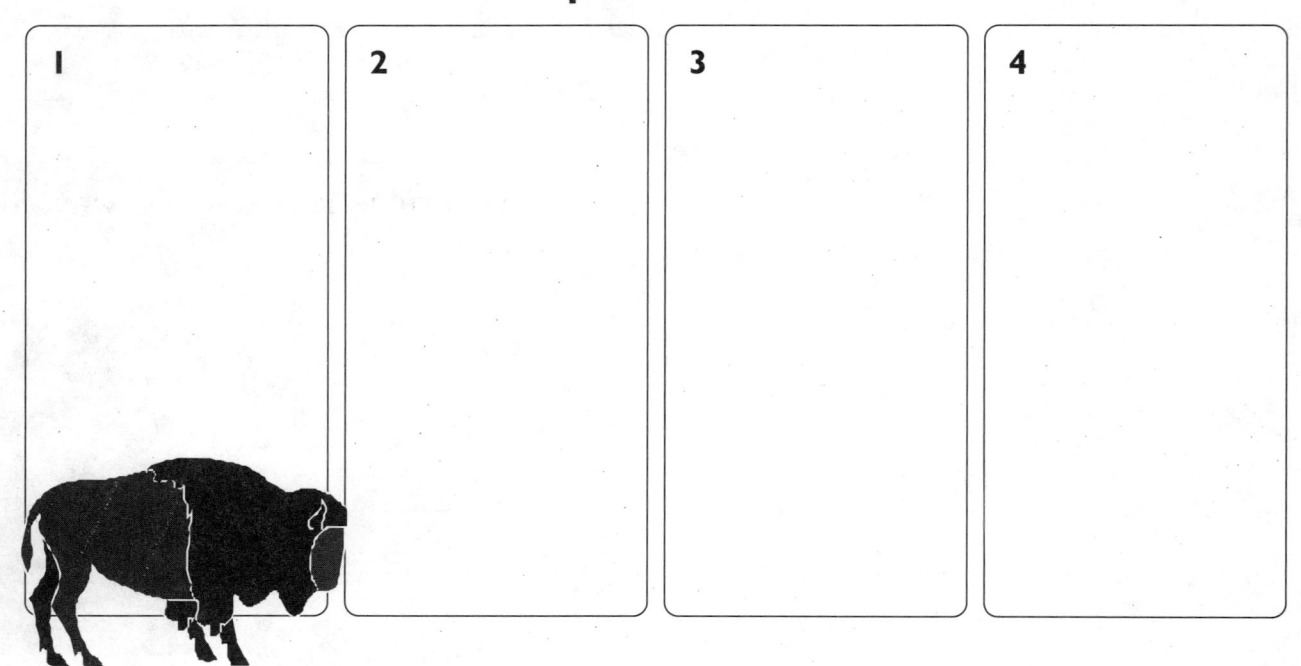

Understanding Sequence of Events

Keep track of the main events of the folktale in a sequence chart. Complete the one below as you listen to the folktale for the second time.

Sequence Chart

1	2	3	4

Listening Skills 4

20

© 2000 Options Publishing, Inc. No part of this document may be reproduced without the written permission of the publisher

Understanding Character

Write a word or phrase about each character based on the story.

Character Chart

Character	Personality	Evidence
Magpie		
Water Turtle	proud	
Neika		

Response

Drawing Conclusions

1. Write a few sentences explaining who the cleverest and smartest creatures in the story were. Give examples from the story of clever things they did.

   _____
   _____
   _____

2. Write a few sentences telling why the people wear the beautiful feathers of the birds, but do not hunt them.

   _____
   _____
   _____

21

Listening Skills 4

LESSON 11 Listening to a Folktale

Why Bat is an Animal

Folktales often tell about animal characters with very different personalities. One may be wise and one foolish, or one may be helpful and the other mean. The folktale you will hear in this lesson is about two groups of animals. Each has a strong leader, but only one of them is wise.

Tips for Listening

- Follow the events of the folktale in your mind — sort out what they mean later.
- Try to picture the events in your mind as the folktale is told.
- Think about each character's personality as he or she is introduced. Look for similarities and differences in their personalities.

Listen and Think

Listen as your teacher reads the folktale, "Why Bat is an Animal"

Here is a vocabulary word you may need to know from the folktale.

ridicule — to laugh at

Understanding Sequence of Events

Keep track of the main events of the folktale in a sequence chart. Complete the one below as you listen to the folktale for the second time.

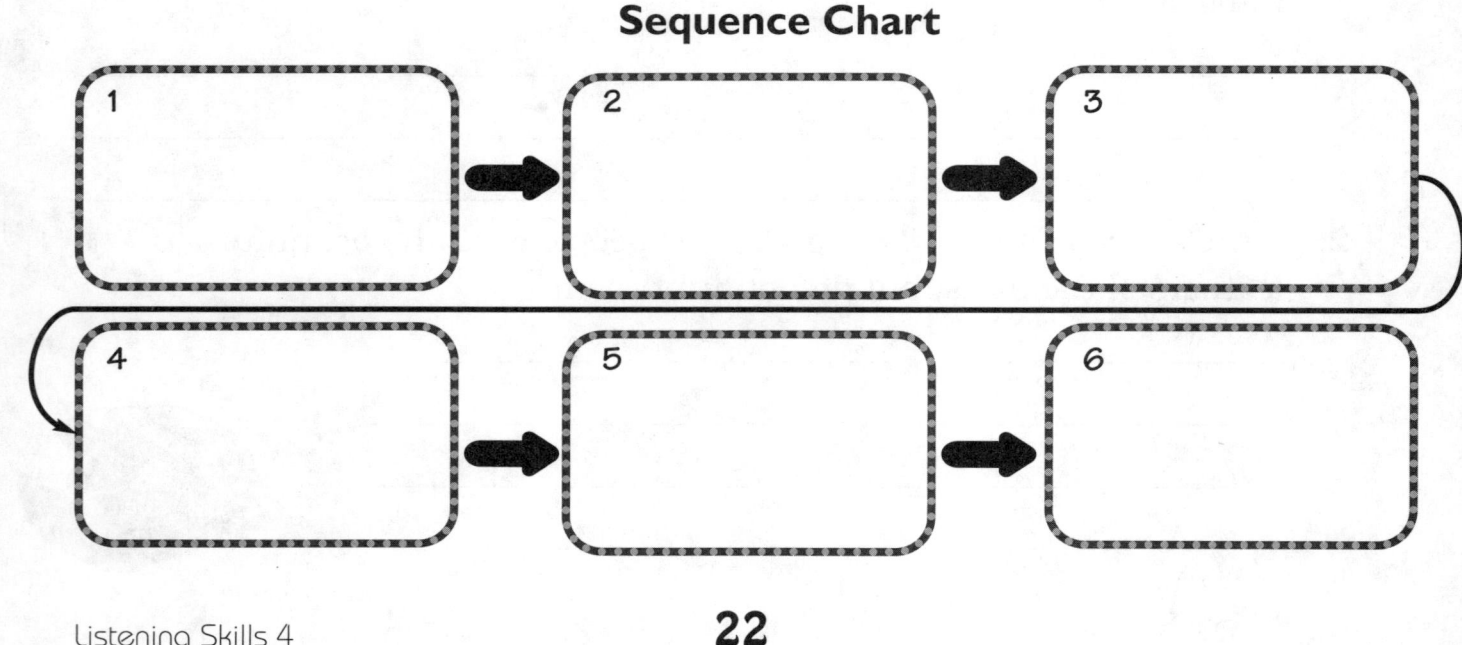

Sequence Chart

1 → 2 → 3
4 → 5 → 6

Listening Skills 4

22

Understanding Character

Character Chart

Character	Personality	Evidence
Crane	Mean	
Bear		
Bat	Smart	

Response

Comparing and Contrasting

1. Write a sentence of two about the difference between birds and animals. Include examples from the story, and one that is not mentioned in the story.

   _____
   _____
   _____

2. Bat has special characteristics that set him apart from all other animals. Write a sentence or two about the special characteristics of a bat.

   _____
   _____
   _____

Listening Skills 4

LESSON

12 Listening to a Folktale

The Boy Who Snared the Wind

Folktales are passed down by word of mouth from generation to generation. They often tell about how people struggle with nature. In this lesson you will hear a folktale about a boy who wrestles with the wind.

Tips for Listening
- Picture the events of the folktale in your mind as the folktale is told.
- Look directly at the speaker and nod your head once in a while to show you understand.

Listen and Think

Listen as your teacher reads the folktale, "The Boy Who Snared the Wind."

Here are the vocabulary words you need to know from the folktale.

ravaged — destroyed, ruined

noose — a loop in rope made with a slipknot so that the loop tightens as the rope is pulled.

Understanding Story Elements

As you listen to "The Boy Who Snared the Wind" for a second time, keep track of story elements using the charts on this page and the next.

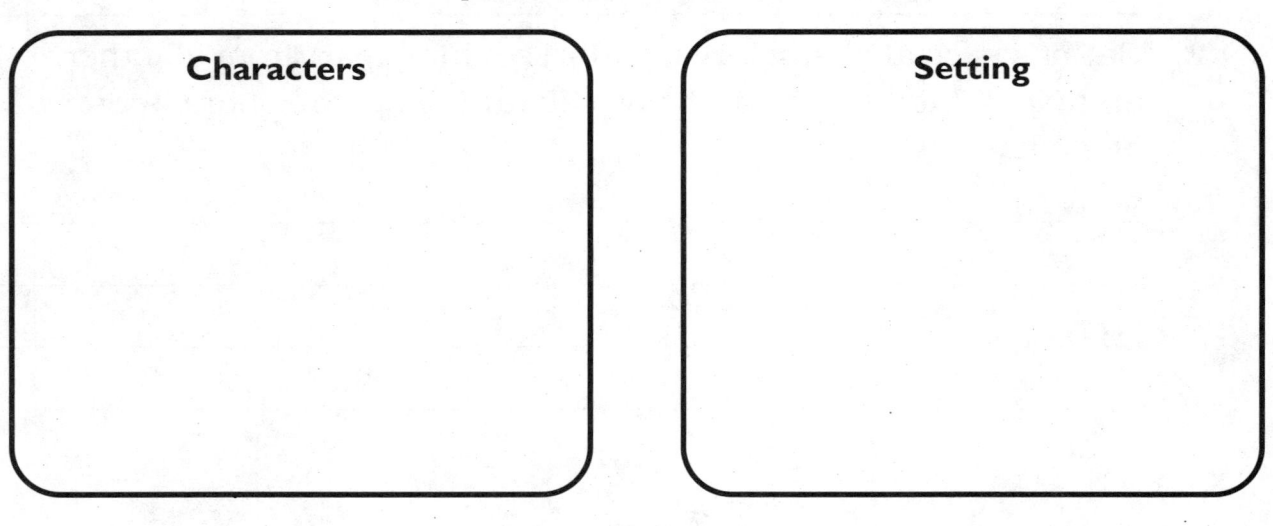

The Boy Who Snared the Wind

Characters	Setting

Listening Skills 4

24

The Boy Who Snared the Wind

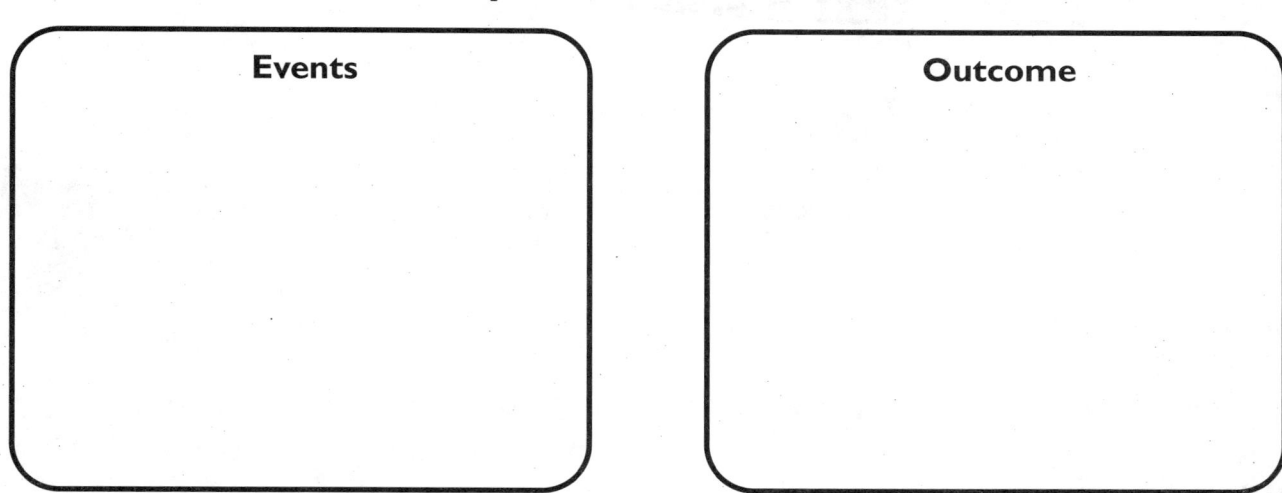

Events

Outcome

Response

Understanding Character

1. Below are some words that describe Sna-naz. Choose two, and write a few sentences telling why they are good words to describe Sna-naz.

    brave   **persistent**   **clever**

_____
_____
_____

2. _____
_____
_____

3. _____
_____
_____

Lesson 13 Practice Test

Fat Sheep, Lean Sheep, and Senor Coyote

Directions

In this part of the test, you will listen to a folktale called Fat Sheep, Lean Sheep, and Senor Coyote. Then you will answer some questions to show how well you understood what was read.

You will listen to the folktale twice. The first time you hear the folktale, listen carefully but do not take notes. As you listen to the folktale the second time, you may want to take notes. You may use these notes to answer the questions that follow. Use the space below for your notes.

Here are some spanish words you will need to know as you listen to the folktale.

flaco — thin

gordo — fat

tablas — tie

Tips for Listening and Note Taking

- Let your imagination help you. You remember more when you let your mind make a picture of the setting, characters, and action.
- Organize your notes around the **five w** and **h**-questions: who? what? when? where? why? and how?

Notes

Here is an example of what your notes might look like using the **five w** and **h**-questions.

Who?	fat sheep, lean sheep, and coyote
What?	
Where?	
When?	one day
Why?	Coyote thinks he will have fun with the stupid sheep
How?	

Listening Skills 4

1. The story you have just heard can be organized into three parts. The conversation between the coyote and sheep happened first. The race came second, and the outcome came last. Write words or phrases to tell what happened during each part.

Fat Sheep, Lean Sheep, and Senor Coyote

The Conversation	The Race	The Outcome

2. Explain why Coyote's thought, "I will have some fun with these stupid sheep," is a mistake or error in judgement.

_____
_____
_____
_____
_____
_____
_____
_____
_____

Listening Skills 4

3. Senor Coyote tries to trick the sheep, but gets tricked himself in the end. Write a short paragraph telling how the sheep avoid being eaten by Coyote.

_____
_____
_____
_____
_____
_____
_____
_____
_____
_____
_____
_____
_____
_____
_____
_____
_____
_____

Answer

4. In what way did Senor Coyote act like a bully? Write a short essay about what it is like to handle someone who acts like a bully. Use examples from the story, from other stories you are familiar with, or from your own experience.

   Check your writing for spelling, grammar, capitalization, and punctuation.

BROOKLYN PUBLIC LIBRARY
3 4444 82239 6438

J 372.6 L
Control #: ocm60491414
Listening Skills : Level 4

6438   83   12/14/07
BROOKLYN PUBLIC LIBRARY
CLINTON HILL BRANCH
380 WASHINGTON AVENUE

Return this material on or before **DUE DATE** to any agency of the Brooklyn Public Library System. A charge is made for each day, including Sundays and holidays, that this item is overdue. Your library card can be revoked for failure to return library materials.

Cat. No. OP0676

OPTIONS
PUBLISHING
inc.

P.O. Box 1749
Merrimack, NH 03054-1749
TOLL FREE 800-782-7300 • FAX 603-424-4056